DENNIS & GNASHER

MIND-BLOWING

MAZES

Can you find your way through the maze before Smithy lands?

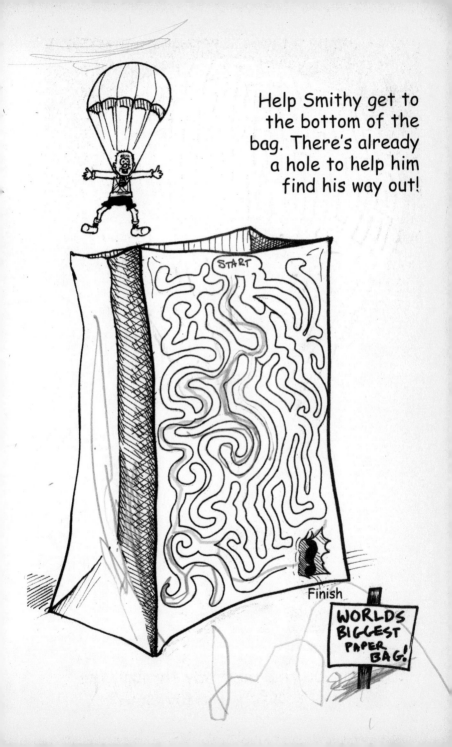

The school bus has to go through the maze.
If it's late, the children will get lines.

Can you dribble the ball from your goal...

...into the other goal and score?

Help Dan find his way to the end of the maze. He can't eat any cow pie until he reaches the end.

Find your way through the forest...but look out for bears!

Hold on tight, you've a rough ride through the mine. Can you make it out the other side?

Rover needs to find his way through the maze.
If he gets to the other end, he will get a
bone.

Minnie needs to make her escape before she gets a new hairdo.

le finish

* Le Start *

Can you make it from the kitchen to the finish. There's a slap-up meal waiting at the other end.

Take a wrong turn on this assault course and you could find yourself back at the beginning.

Can you find your
way through the
runways and back
to the airport?

FINISH

START

You'll have to go through this maze
quietly...you don't want the tiger to hear you.

Can you make it to the finish and escape from Dennis's snoring?

If you find your way to the end of the maze, Plug will have the longest jump.

Find your way to the finish
and you'll be the star.

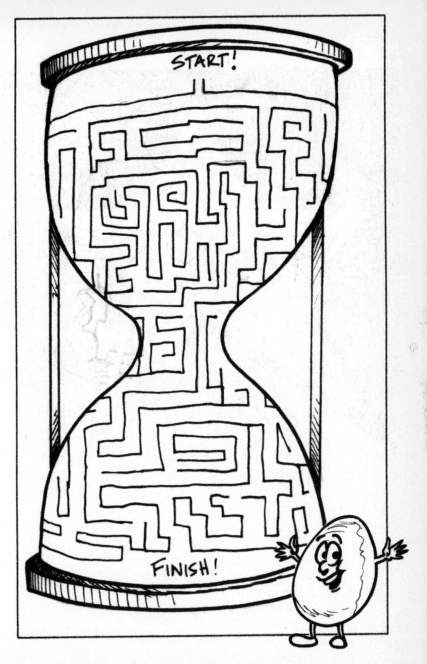

Find the finish before time runs out.

You'll have a whale of a time in this maze.

Dennis and Gnasher need to make it to the finish before the last dromedary leaves.

Dennis has gone down under, mate.
Find your way to the end before
his boomerang comes back.

Get to the end and the ice-cream's all yours!

Find your way to the finish and help Minnie change the tune.

Can you make it through this maze without disturbing Gnasher?

Find your way to the tower and rescue the
princess but watch out for the
dungeons...there's no escape!

START

WATER BOMB!

Help Dennis find the water bombs and then you can look for the softies.

Help Dennis and Gnasher find their way out of the haunted house.

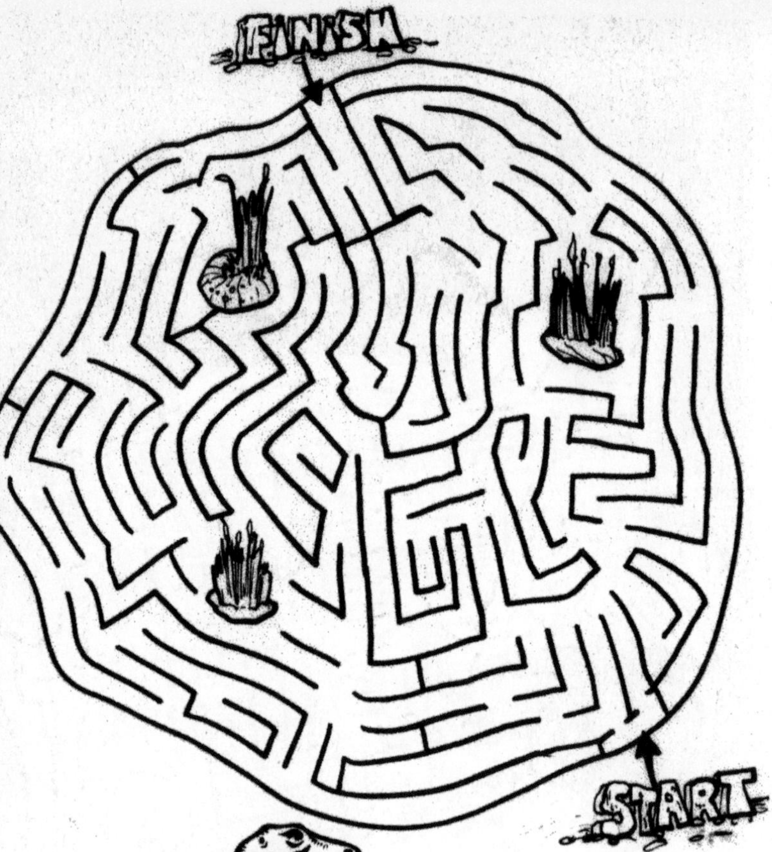

FINISH

START

You'll need to move quickly to keep ahead of the dinosaur, it's hungry.

Elephants never forget but can you remember
the way from start to finish?

FINISH!

START

Can you make it to the finish before the ice-cream melts?

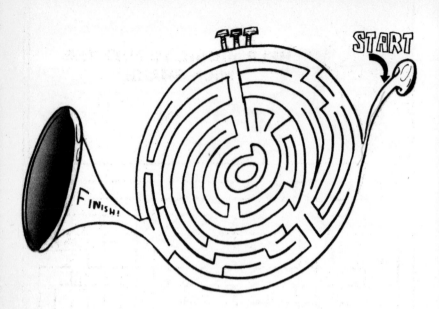

Can you make it out of the maze before the Bash Street band starts to 'play'?

HELP MINNIE TO FIND THE MILK SHAKE.

Help the mouse make it to the cheese
without springing the trap.

Find your way through the maze and you can help the professor spot the UFO.

FINISH

Start

Find your way to the finish and you can ride the wave back to the beach.

Can you help Old Mother Hubbard find her way through the maze?

You have to make it through the maze before the fuse burns out!

Dennis's dad just needs to find his way through the maze and then he can make Dennis do the rest of the gardening. No wonder Dennis isn't happy!

The maze labels read: **START!** and **FINISH!**

Find your way through the maze and help Danny win the shot put competition.

Fatty is so hungry! Can you make it to the finish before he eats the cake?

If you make it to the finish, the ship will see you and you can leave the island. Will your sleepy friend wake in time?

The art gallery is very big with many long corridors but there is only one way out. Can you make your way all the way through?

If you can get from the start to the finish,
Walter can have his teddy.

Howzatt! Will Dennis bowl you out?

The candle is burning down. Can you find your way to the finish while there is still some light?

The hippo is right behind you. Can you make it to the finish and out of the water before it catches you?

This tree house is getting shaky. Can you find your way to the finish before it falls down?

You need to find your way out of
this prickly situation.

You'll need to mouse your way through this maze.

Don't get the hump if you can't find your way.

Find your way to the
finish and you can
open the presents.

You'll need to go right through this maze to check you're getting a nice little runner.

Can you find your way to the end before the snowman melts?

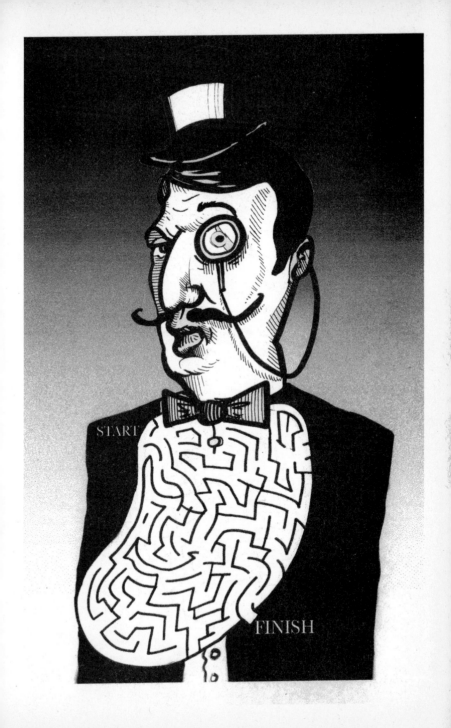

Can you make it all the way through
this extra large burger?

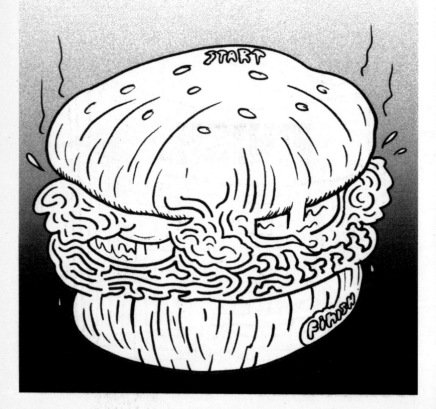

These hip-hop kids need your
help with a tiptop maze.

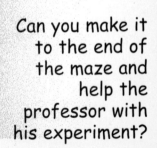

Can you make it to the end of the maze and help the professor with his experiment?

Dennis needs someone to push him but you need to find your way through the maze first.

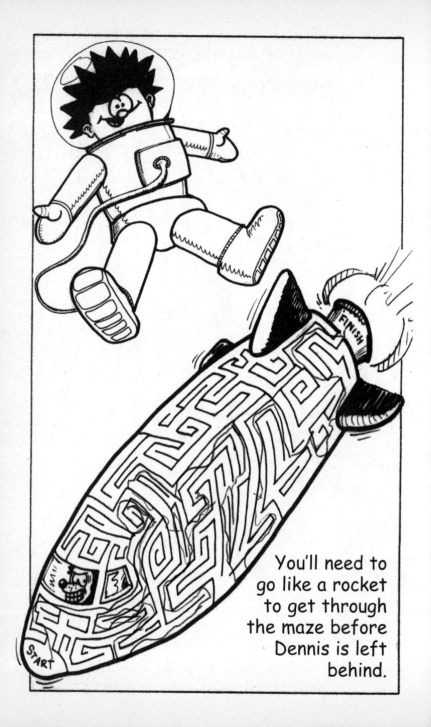

This maze will lead  a strike.

Dennis isn't very keen on this new jumper but he needs you to find your way through the maze before he can change back into his old one.

Find your way through this maze and then you can draw your own picture.

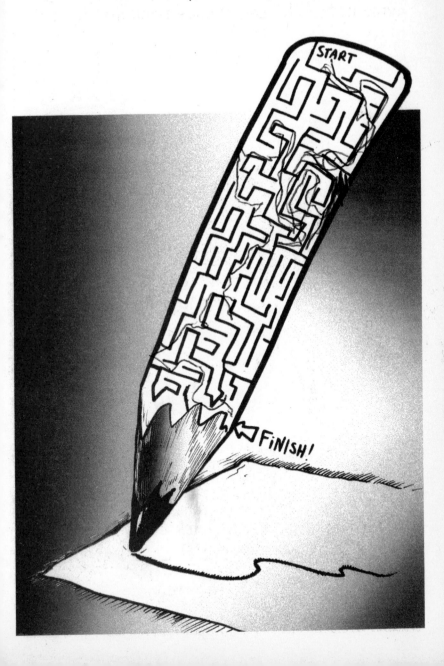

START

FINISH

Can you make it to the finish of the maze and
then help land the flying carpet?

Big Wheels is heading straight for you.
Make it through the maze so you don't get
flattened.

Can you find your way to the finish? You'll save the farmer's bacon if you can!

Dan doesn't want to make any wrong turns, can you help him find his way through the tunnel?

Dan's worked up a big appetite. You'll need to be quick to make it through the maze before he's finished the whole cow pie.

Dennis is tough but not tough enough to beat the whole team himself. Can you make it to second down before they catch up with him?

Make it to the finish without any wrong turns
to dodge detention.

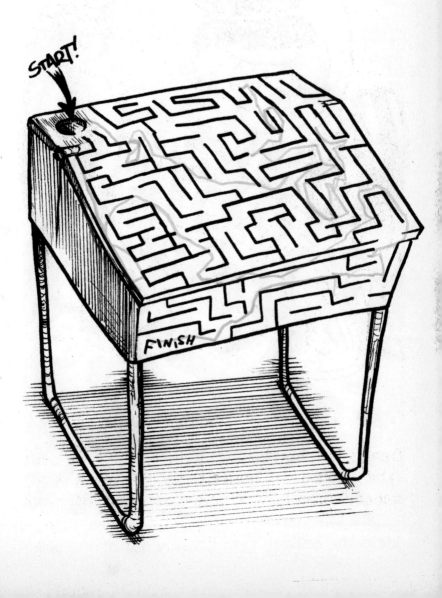

START!

Help the badger find his way out of his set.

This is a strange post box! Guide the letter to the finish so that it doesn't get stuck down a dead end.

Rasher may love his swill but Walter can't stand it.
Help Walter find the finish so he can go home for a
nice bubble bath.

FINISH

START→

This is a difficult
course. Can you
make it to the
finish without
getting lost?

Dennis loves playing his drums. He's very loud but not very good. If you're quick, you can make it to the finish before he starts playing.